My Loos

By Maria Fleming

My tooth is loose.
But it won't fall out.

On Monday, I wiggled it. I jiggled it.
But my tooth would not fall out. ③

On Tuesday, I wiggled it. I jiggled it.
But my tooth would not fall out.

On Wednesday, I wiggled it. I jiggled it. But my tooth would not fall out. (5)

On Thursday, I wiggled it. I jiggled it.
But my tooth would not fall out.

On Friday, I did not wiggle it.
I did not jiggle it.
Can you guess what happened? (7)

My tooth fell out!
Hooray!